ASHTA

Written by Alicia Racela

Illustrated by Nia Ling

Published by TwinFlame Ventures, LLC

This first book is dedicated to my two children Malia and Miles who inspire me to live life authentically, with joy, curiosity and love in every moment.

And to my love Donnell, the fierce spirit that dances with my soul, gratitude for your support as we continue to create magic together.

Ashta is an octopus that represents our crown chakra. We witness her brilliance and learn about her unique gifts as she introduces us to the connection we share with all living things through love. A we travel through her home in the ocean, Ashta teaches us the benefits of mindfulness and reminds us to believe in our own magic.

The Crown Chakra is located at the top of the head. It is a big circle and is associated with the beautiful color of violet. The Crown Chakra is the center of thought and wisdom, while connecting us with the universe. It is the energy center in our bodies that is open to our fullest potential.

Ashtanga represents the eight limbs of a spiritual practice based in the philosophy and science of yoga. These eight limbs include, the laws of life, the rules of living, meditation, breathwork, physical postures, withdrawal from the senses, focus of attention, and the settled mind.

I love jetting through the coral reefs, as they have layers to explore.

I can swim to the surface, even climb on to land, but my home is usually on the ocean floor.

I was born into a large family and chose a great life on my own.

I make friends of all colors and sizes everywhere that I roam.

I'm here to share my story, so join me on this ride.

My name is Ashta, lets go explore and flow with the tide.

There are so many sides of me that I create a buzz that vibrates through the ocean.

Who is she?

How does she disappear?

Do her eight arms improve her motion?

My intelligence is immeasurable. I still surprise those who study me.

Whether it is a shark, or a curious visitor from land,

I have more talents than even they can see.

I am mysterious and I fool my predators every day.

I can adjust to any situation,

I also hide in plain sight from my prey.

I meditate before I sleep, so my mind and body grow.

I am at my best for my next adventure. Who knows where I will go.

I have a brain in eac[h] arm, and one in my head above my mantle.

As I gather information from m[y] surroundings, I quick[ly] learn what I can handle.

With my great memory, I understand the consequences of my choices and actions from the past.

Being present and aware of my surroundings, I adapt with color changing disguises that shift quickly and don't last.

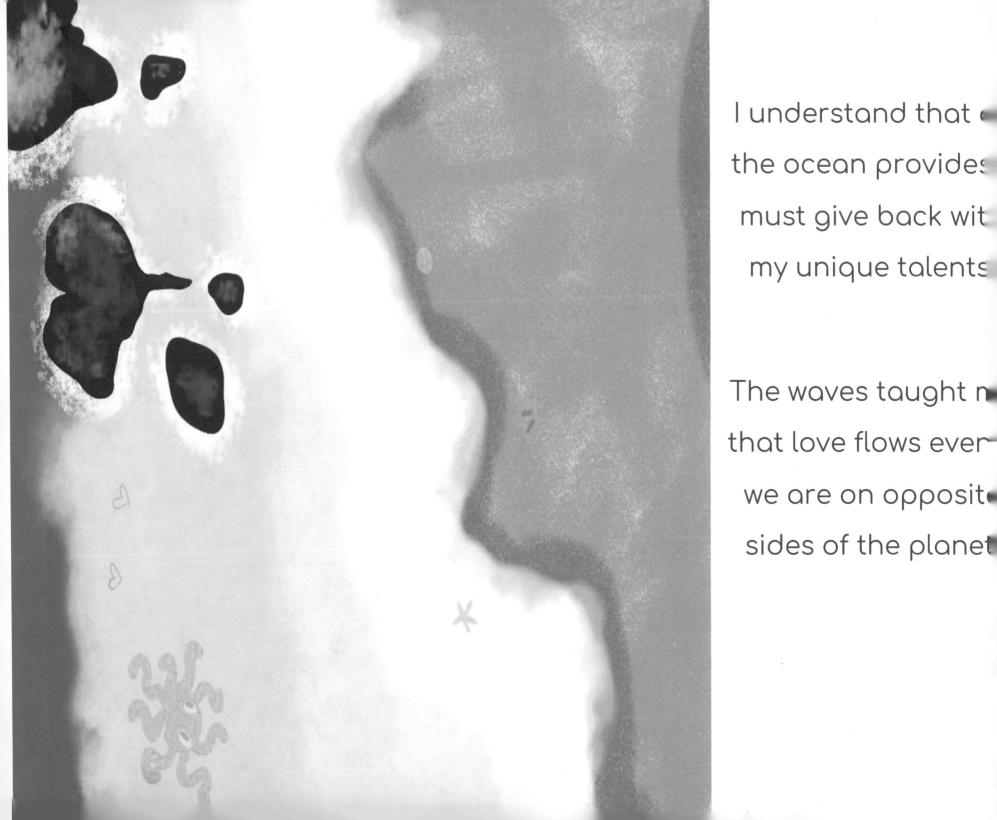

I understand that
the ocean provides
must give back wit
my unique talents

The waves taught m
that love flows ever
we are on opposit
sides of the planet

We all have a purpose
for our life. It takes
time for some to find.

Trust in your miracle
existence and maintain
the peace in your mind.

Take in a deep
breath, as I bring
oxygen into my
gills.

Let's exhale slowly,
pinky promise, and
be open to life's
thrills.

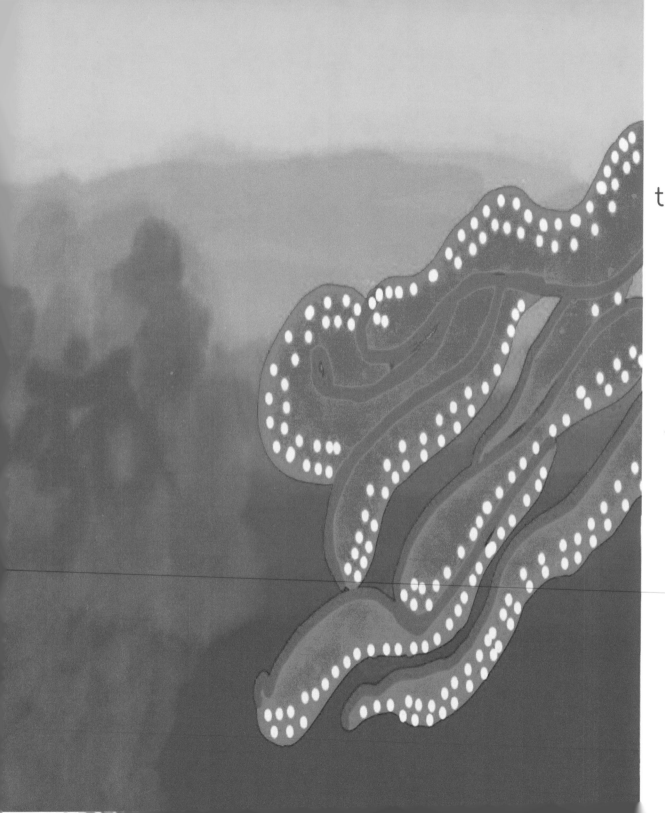

I leave you now with
the universal vibration
of OM.

Please come back to
visit and we can take
an exploration of my
home.

NAMASTE

NOTES

What is your favorite animal in the Ocean?

How can we take better care of the Ocean?

Draw a picture of ASHTA and YOU!